Reading Comprehension

Book 3

BIGYN C.P. SCHOOL
LLANELLI, DYFED SA15 1DH

Jo Browning Wroe
David Lambert

Permission to photocopy

This book contains worksheets which may be reproduced by photocopier or other means for use by the purchaser. This permission is granted on the understanding that these copies will be used within the educational establishment of the purchaser. This book and all its contents remain copyright. Copies may be made without reference to the publisher or the licensing scheme for the making of photocopies operated by the Publishers' Licensing Agency.

The rights of Jo Browning Wroe and David Lambert to be identified as authors of this work have been asserted by them in accordance with sections 77 and 78 of the Copyright, Designs and Patents Act 1988.

Reading Comprehension Book 3
LL05033
ISBN 1 85503 383 6
© Jo Browning Wroe and David Lambert
Cover illustrations © Lizzie Finlay, Sally Launder and David Pattison
Illustrations © Lizzie Finlay, Sally Launder, David Pattison and Caroline Sharpe
All rights reserved
First published 2003

Printed in the UK for LDA
Duke Street, Wisbech, Cambs, PE13 2AE UK
3195 Wilson Drive NW, Grand Rapids, MI 49544 USA

Contents

Teacher's notes

Each book in the LDA Reading Comprehension series provides up to 33 stimulating photocopiable comprehension activities for the children you teach. In line with the National Literacy Strategy, the books present a wide variety of text types, including newspaper articles, poetry, dialogue, prose, instructions, charts and tables, letters, guidebook information and journal entries.

The activities are graded so that you will find a general trend of increasing conceptual complexity or discoursal organisation within the texts as you move through each section.

The four skill areas

To develop and hone your pupils' skills in four crucial areas of reading comprehension, the activities are grouped under the following headings:

Getting the main idea

In these activities, the pupils' overall grasp of the text is tested. To answer the questions, they are required to use their overall understanding of the text's main theme, argument or development.

Making inferences

The questions in this section encourage the pupils to make connections between the discrete elements embedded in the text. Pupils must choose, from a range of possibilities, the answer that is most likely to be true.

Noting details

Here, pupils are invited to scan the text for information and to retrieve discrete facts, for example an opening time, a date, or a figure. Occasionally, a more systematic reading is required to grasp the relationship between facts embedded in the text.

Using context clues

The questions in these activities encourage pupils to be sleuths, searching the textual environment for clues in order to select the most appropriate words or phrases to fill the blanks and complete the passage.

The questions

For each activity there are five questions that relate directly to the text. In most cases these are multiple choice and pupils simply have to circle the letters to indicate their answers. For the Noting details activities, pupils are required to write in their own answers.

At the end of each activity, there is a sixth, open-ended extension question. This is designed to encourage further reading, research, reflection or creativity on the same topic or a related one. These questions aim to personalise the text, making the issues raised within it relevant to the reader. There are three types of extension question:

Ask yourself

These questions tend to have an ethical slant and seek to develop pupils' critical thinking skills. For example, after an article about vegetarians:

Is it right to kill animals for their meat? Is it right to farm animals for their milk or eggs?

Find out for yourself

These questions put the pupils in charge of their learning, inviting them to find out more about a subject. This might be done in a number of different ways, for example by using books, searching on the Web or asking people questions. It is usually left to the pupil to identify their own sources of reference, as each of these questions is very much a point of departure, not an end in itself. For example, following a text about a mountain rescue:

In what different situations can people get into danger and need to be rescued? What ways are there to find or rescue people? How can trained animals or technology be helpful?

Express yourself

These questions encourage pupils to respond imaginatively and creatively to the texts they have read. They might be asked to write prose or poetry or to draw, design or make something. For example:

Think of a place where you have spent a good holiday or choose a place you would like to visit. Write a short holiday brochure to attract people to your holiday destination.

How do I use the book?

These Reading Comprehension books are intended to be a flexible teaching resource to use in the way that best enhances the learning going on in your classroom. The activities will fit well into the small group section of the literacy hour, but this is by no means the only appropriate context for the material. At the beginning of a school year, for example, they could be used as a tool to assess your pupils' level of comprehension and to find if there are particular areas of weakness which can then be addressed.

The texts should take no longer than 10 minutes to read and the questions no more than another 10 minutes to complete, although this will vary greatly from pupil to pupil.

In some circumstances, it may be beneficial for pupils to tackle the activities in pairs. In this way, less able pupils who lack confidence can provide each other with support as they read and then answer the questions.

There might also be occasions when it is helpful for a pupil to have access to the answers, in order to check their own work.

Answers

An answer key is provided at the back of the book on page 64.

Up and Away

Have you ever wondered how a heavy jumbo jet, laden with over 700 passengers and all their luggage, can get off the ground and fly through the air? To gather speed along the runway, the plane is pushed forward by its jet engines. This is called 'thrust'. But how does this help the plane take to the air? It is all to do with air pressure. You can do a little experiment to see how it works.

Take a sheet of paper and hold it to your mouth, like this.

Now blow over it. You will notice that the paper rises up. This is because when you blow, it reduces the air pressure above the paper. There is now greater air pressure underneath the sheet and this pushes the paper up. This is exactly what happens to a plane. As it races along the runway, the air streaming over the top of the wings reduces the air pressure – just as when you blow over a sheet of paper. The air pressure underneath the wing is now greater and it lifts the plane up. This effect is called 'lift'. It is what gets a heavy jumbo jet airborne.

Up and Away

Read the text carefully and circle the best ending for each sentence.

1 'Thrust' comes from
   a) the jet engines.
   b) air pressure.
   c) the runway.

2 The experiment shows
   a) how hard you can blow.
   b) how light a sheet of paper is.
   c) what makes a plane take off.

3 'Lift' is created by
   a) the air under the wing pushing downwards.
   b) the air under the wing pushing upwards.
   c) the air over the wing pushing upwards.

4 'Airborne' means
   a) in the air.
   b) lighter than air.
   c) like air.

5 The text is about
   a) air safety.
   b) jumbo jets.
   c) how planes fly.

Express yourself

Imagine you are the pilot or a passenger on a jumbo jet. Describe the view from the cockpit or the passenger window from 9,000 metres. What can you see below? What can you see in the sky?

Hungry World Sponsored Walk

Information for walkers

Please read this carefully before the walk and bring it with you on the day.

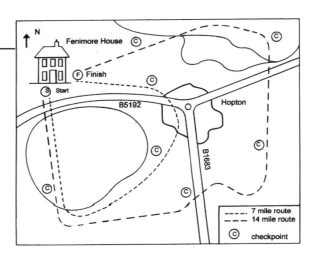

The start

The walk starts and finishes at Fenimore House, 3 miles west of Hopton on the B5192. Walkers must choose between 7-mile and 14-mile routes. (See map.)

Registration is from 8 a.m. On arrival, go straight to the Registration desk, where you will receive your walker number.

Note: we regret the routes are not suitable for wheelchairs or pushchairs. Dogs are welcome on the walk, but must be kept on a lead at all times.

Along the route

Keep to the routes marked at all times. Checkpoint marshals are stationed along the routes at points marked on the map. You will need to give your walker number at each checkpoint. If you cannot complete your route for any reason, please let a marshal know.

All walkers must finish their routes and return to Fenimore House by 6 p.m., when safety cover ceases.

Safety cover

There will be police cover on both routes throughout the day and first aid will be provided by the Hopton St John Ambulance.

Clothing and equipment

Wear strong, flat-soled shoes or boots. Bring plenty of sunblock cream – and pack waterproofs, just in case! Please ensure that you also bring with you any medication you are likely to need, e.g. asthma inhaler, hay fever tablets.

Refreshments

At the start, the first 1,000 walkers can collect a free bottle of water and chocolate bar, courtesy of the Co-operative Group. Snacks and drinks will be sold at all checkpoints.

Sponsorship money

When you have collected all your sponsorship money, please send a cheque to: Claire Dunne, Hungry World Sponsored Walk, Fenimore House, Hopton, Ho2 WS5.

Hungry World Sponsored Walk

Read the text carefully and circle the best ending for each sentence.

1. Marshals are probably
   a) other walkers.
   b) people who help and direct the walkers.
   c) police.

2. Safety cover is probably to
   a) protect walkers from the rain.
   b) help anyone who is hurt or in difficulty.
   c) stop people breaking the law.

3. The sponsored walk organisers
   a) think it will be sunny.
   b) think it will rain.
   c) do not know what the weather will be like.

4. Walkers can buy food
   a) at the checkpoints.
   b) from the Co-op.
   c) at Fenimore House.

5. The purpose of the sponsored walk is
   a) to help people get exercise.
   b) to raise money for charity.
   c) to stop walkers being hungry.

Find out for yourself

Find out about different ways you can raise money for charity.

Film Review

* Give it a miss
** OK if you have nothing better to do
*** Worth seeing
**** Don't miss it

JOHNNY ENGLISH
He knows no fear
He knows no pain
He knows Nothing

New Bond spoof is spot on!

It's the film all Rowan Atkinson fans have been waiting for. Britain's highest-paid comic actor returns to the screen in this hilarious spoof of James Bond movies.

Comic genius Rowan Atkinson has carved a career playing eccentrics and misfits (Mr Bean, Blackadder). In *Johnny English*, he plays another unlikely hero, who longs to be the smooth master of espionage – but falls short every time.

Her Majesty's Secret Servant, Johnny English, is a bungling spy who manages to stab himself with a tranquilliser dart and set fire to a rug in an Arabian market. When he discovers a dastardly plot to steal the Crown Jewels by smuggling them out in a coffin, Johnny English surprises funeral guests by dancing on the coffin, thinking it contains the jewels. Except it turns out to be a real funeral – and the coffin does not contain the jewels at all! But despite the dreadful mistakes and a string of embarrassing moments, English somehow manages to come out on top in the end.

The film has excellent supporting performances from Natalie Imbruglia in her first film role, and John Malkovich as the British agent's arch-enemy, the mad Frenchman, Monsieur Sauvage. A 'must see' for all the family.

Our rating ****   Johnny English (PG) opens at cinemas nationwide on 11 April.

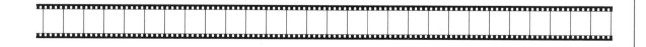

Film Review

Read the text carefully and circle the best ending for each sentence.

1. On 11 April, Johnny English will be shown
   a) in cinemas all over the UK.
   b) all over the world.
   c) on widescreen TVs in the UK.

2. The rating system is for showing
   a) what readers think of the film.
   b) what the reviewer thinks of the film.
   c) that the reviewer likes the film.

3. The word 'spoof' means it is
   a) a spy film.
   b) a popular film.
   c) a comedy imitation of another film.

4. Rowan Atkinson often plays
   a) comic geniuses.
   b) odd characters.
   c) spies.

5. The coffin really contains
   a) nothing.
   b) a dead body.
   c) the Crown Jewels.

Express yourself

Write a review of a film you have seen recently.

Ali's Reply

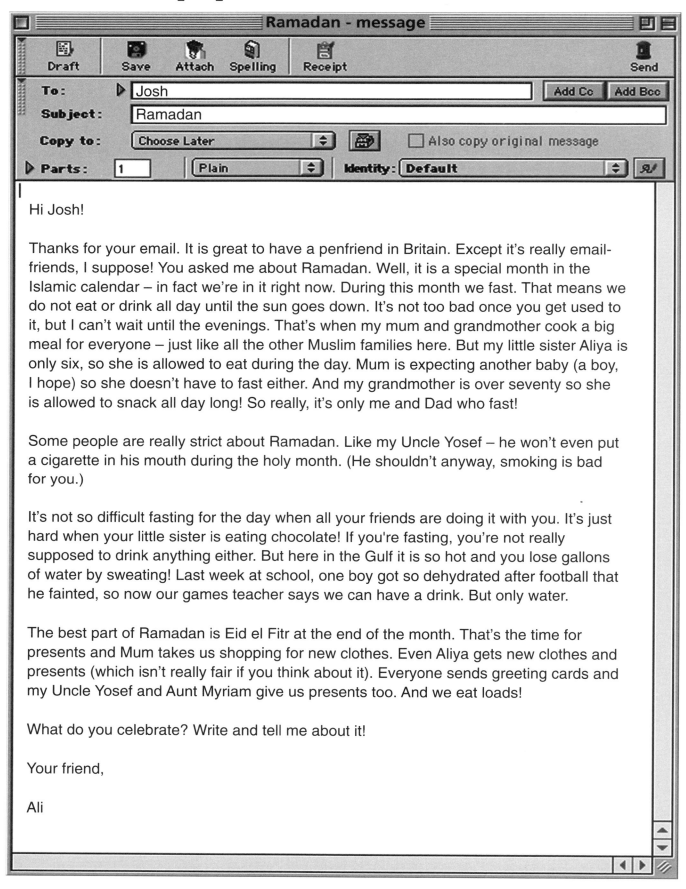

Ramadan - message

Draft   Save   Attach   Spelling   Receipt   Send

To: ▷ Josh   Add Cc   Add Bcc

Subject: Ramadan

Copy to: Choose Later   ☐ Also copy original message

▷ Parts: 1   Plain   Identity: Default

Hi Josh!

Thanks for your email. It is great to have a penfriend in Britain. Except it's really email-friends, I suppose! You asked me about Ramadan. Well, it is a special month in the Islamic calendar – in fact we're in it right now. During this month we fast. That means we do not eat or drink all day until the sun goes down. It's not too bad once you get used to it, but I can't wait until the evenings. That's when my mum and grandmother cook a big meal for everyone – just like all the other Muslim families here. But my little sister Aliya is only six, so she is allowed to eat during the day. Mum is expecting another baby (a boy, I hope) so she doesn't have to fast either. And my grandmother is over seventy so she is allowed to snack all day long! So really, it's only me and Dad who fast!

Some people are really strict about Ramadan. Like my Uncle Yosef – he won't even put a cigarette in his mouth during the holy month. (He shouldn't anyway, smoking is bad for you.)

It's not so difficult fasting for the day when all your friends are doing it with you. It's just hard when your little sister is eating chocolate! If you're fasting, you're not really supposed to drink anything either. But here in the Gulf it is so hot and you lose gallons of water by sweating! Last week at school, one boy got so dehydrated after football that he fainted, so now our games teacher says we can have a drink. But only water.

The best part of Ramadan is Eid el Fitr at the end of the month. That's the time for presents and Mum takes us shopping for new clothes. Even Aliya gets new clothes and presents (which isn't really fair if you think about it). Everyone sends greeting cards and my Uncle Yosef and Aunt Myriam give us presents too. And we eat loads!

What do you celebrate? Write and tell me about it!

Your friend,

Ali

Ali's Reply

Read the text carefully and circle the best ending for each sentence.

1. During Ramadan, Muslims fast
   a) overnight for a month.
   b) during the day for a month.
   c) night and day for a month.

2. Ali's mother does not have to fast because
   a) she has to cook.
   b) she's too old.
   c) she is pregnant.

3. Uncle Yosef does not smoke during Ramadan because
   a) it is bad for him.
   b) he is a strict Muslim.
   c) it saves money.

4. 'Dehydrated' means the body does not have enough
   a) water.
   b) food.
   c) exercise.

5. Ali doesn't think his sister should get presents and new clothes because
   a) she is younger than him.
   b) she is a girl.
   c) she hasn't fasted during Ramadan.

Find out for yourself

Find out about another religious festival. It could be Christian, Jewish, Hindu or Buddhist. How is it celebrated?

John Lennon

John Lennon was born in 1940 in the city of Liverpool in the north of England. When he was only 15, he and four other boys formed a pop group which later became world famous. Together they shaped the history of pop music. During the 1960s, the Beatles, by then a group of four, had hit after hit all over the world. In some countries, young people could not name or recognise their president, but they knew the names and faces of the four lads from Liverpool: John, Paul, George and Ringo. By the 1970s the 'Fab Four', as the Beatles were also known, had broken up and gone their separate ways. John Lennon continued to perform songs that he wrote with his wife, Yoko Ono. Many were love songs, but after becoming involved in the campaign against the war in Vietnam, he sang more about peace and an end to all war.

In December 1980, tragedy struck. As John and Yoko were returning to their apartment in the Dakota Building in New York, a crazed fan approached them in the street. John was used to people asking him for his autograph and so probably did not think it strange. Before anyone could stop him, the young man, who had been waiting all day for Lennon, pulled out a gun and shot him dead. The news of John Lennon's death shocked millions around the world. It was a sad loss for everyone who grew up with his music.

John Lennon

Read the text carefully and circle the best ending for each sentence.

⟨1⟩   The Beatles
- a) studied the history of pop music.
- b) invented pop music.
- c) helped to make pop music what it is today.

⟨2⟩   In the 1970s, the Beatles
- a) went to live in America.
- b) split up.
- c) had many more hits.

⟨3⟩   Later in his career, John
- a) stopped writing songs.
- b) stopped writing love songs.
- c) started writing songs against war.

⟨4⟩   When he was killed, John and Yoko were
- a) going home.
- b) going out.
- c) in their apartment.

⟨5⟩   John probably thought the man
- a) was crazy.
- b) wanted to get his autograph.
- c) wanted to shoot him.

Find out more for yourself

Listen to John Lennon's song 'Imagine'. What is it about?

The Stash

'Rick! Rick! Wait … I've dropped something … I've got to go back for it!'

But Rick was not going to stop. All Jack could hear was the sound of his friend's burly body ploughing through the bushes to get as far away from the old house as possible. He was gone, and with him the torch. Who could blame him? It was not the sort of place you hung around. Not with what they'd just discovered stashed up in a front room. Whoever it was would be back for it. He should leg it like Rick. But he had to return.

Jack put his foot on the bottom step. He heard it creak and the noise echo through the empty house. It made his heart thump even harder in his chest. He waited with his foot there. Cold winter moonlight was coming in through the dusty window at the top of the staircase. It fell on the rotten floorboards and showed up the nails on the staircase where a carpet had once been. He hesitated. No, he had to go up and get his sweatshirt back. He had tied it around his waist and it must have fallen off on the landing as he and Rick ran out. Or perhaps as he had opened the cupboard where he and Rick had seen the thick wads – piles of them, each bound by a rubber band.

They would know instantly that someone had been in the room, seen their stash. It would not take much to work out that it was a kid from Mayflower School – that logo he'd always been so proud of, the ship sailing on the sea, its sails unfurled! They'd know exactly where to come.

And they would know who to look for, too. Why had Mum always insisted on sewing in name tags? He had to go up. He was about to take the next step when a pale beam of light moved slowly over the high ceiling, as if it was searching for something. Rick! He'd come back! And brought the torch!

That was when Jack heard the car struggling up the hill. It wasn't Rick. They were back …

The Stash

Read the text carefully and circle the best ending for each sentence.

1. The boys had discovered a stash of stolen
   a) drugs.
   b) banknotes.
   c) jewels.

2. Jack had lost his sweatshirt, but
   a) knew exactly where it was.
   b) had some idea of where it might be.
   c) had no idea where it was.

3. He had to get his sweatshirt back because
   a) his mum would be angry.
   b) it was a cold winter night.
   c) it would give him away to the robbers.

4. If anyone found the sweatshirt, they would know
   a) Jack's name.
   b) Jack's school.
   c) Jack's name and school.

5. The light on the ceiling was
   a) his friend returning with the torch.
   b) from car headlamps.
   c) someone switching the hall light on.

Express yourself
What do you think happened next? Continue the story.

Braille

A blind person would not be able to read this page as you are doing now. But the blind can read, and almost as fast as you. How do they do it?

To find the answer we have to go to France and back to the year 1824. A 4-year-old boy called Louis Braille was playing in his father's workshop when he had an accident that left him blind.

To begin with, Louis went to the local school and then to a school for the blind in Paris. It was there, at the age of 15, that he developed the system of reading and writing that would help blind people gain access to the wealth of ideas in the world of books and writing. It became known as Braille. Louis' brilliant idea was to convert every letter of the alphabet into a symbol made up of raised dots on a page. The blind person can run their fingers over these dots from left to right and 'read' each letter. By putting the letters together, a word can be formed. The process is very slow at first but, strange as it may seem, it is no harder to learn to read using your fingers than it is using your eyes.

Today, the blind and the partially sighted can write with electric Braille typewriters that punch dots on the paper. Millions of books are published in Braille. Because the dots have to be quite big and well spaced for the fingers to feel them, a book in Braille is about ten times longer than the same book in print.

Braille

Read the text carefully and circle the best ending for each sentence.

1. Louis Braille
   a) was born blind.
   b) became blind at 4 years old.
   c) became blind at 15 years old.

2. Louis Braille invented a system that
   a) helped other blind people become wealthy.
   b) helped other blind people to read.
   c) gave blind people a chance to see the world.

3. In Braille, a single pattern of dots stands for
   a) a sentence.
   b) a word.
   c) a letter of the alphabet.

4. Learning to read Braille
   a) is more difficult than learning to read print.
   b) is no more difficult than learning to read print.
   c) is faster if you can use your eyes.

5. Compared with printed books, Braille books are generally
   a) thicker.
   b) thinner.
   c) the same size.

Find out for yourself

Find a Braille alphabet. How does it work? Learn to write your name in Braille. You can do this by pressing a pencil point hard into a piece of card to make the dots. (You will feel the dots on the other side.) Take two pieces of card. Write your name in Braille on one and get a friend to write their name on the other card. Close your eyes and use your fingers to read the names. Can you tell which is yours?

Anne Frank

ANNE FRANK was a young Jewish girl living in Frankfurt, Germany, at the time Hitler's Nazi party came to power. Anne's father, Otto Frank, took his family to live in Amsterdam in the Netherlands. Anne lived there quite happily with her parents and sister until 1942, when the Germans invaded the Netherlands. Hitler had ordered all Jews to be rounded up and sent to concentration camps, so the Frank family had to go into hiding. They hid with four other Jews in tiny rooms behind a false wall in Otto Frank's former office. They were kept alive for almost two years by the kindness of a Dutch family who smuggled rations of food to them – at the risk of their own lives.

Anne's remarkable diary records their life in hiding, including the many tensions and arguments between the people sharing the cramped space. But she remained lively and good humoured. At one point in her diary, Anne writes: 'I still believe people are really good at heart.'

But not everyone was so kind. A Dutch informer reported the hiding place. Anne and her family were taken by the Germans and sent to Belsen concentration camp. She died there shortly after, aged only 15. Her father, Otto, was the family's only survivor and after the war he made his daughter's diary available for the world to read.

Anne Frank

Read the text carefully and circle the best ending for each sentence.

1. Anne's family hid because
   a) they were German.
   b) they were Jewish.
   c) they were not Dutch.

2. The kind Dutch family could have
   a) reported Anne's family.
   b) died from lack of food.
   c) been killed for helping Anne's family.

3. The atmosphere in the hiding place was
   a) always good humoured.
   b) never good humoured.
   c) sometimes tense.

4. Anne's family was discovered because
   a) someone told the Germans.
   b) Anne believed people were too kind to hurt them.
   c) the war ended.

5. Anne's diary was published because
   a) she died in the concentration camp.
   b) her father survived and wanted people to read it.
   c) none of the family survived but the diary was found after the war.

Find out for yourself

Anne's diary is published under the title *The Diary of a Young Girl*. See if you can find a copy and then read some of it. Imagine you could write a letter to Anne in her hiding place. What would you tell her? What questions would you ask?

Fabuloso

Come to Fabuloso where the air is clean and life is laid back. It's the perfect place to leave your cares behind. Relax and unwind in style at a luxury hotel. Or get close to nature in a beachside bungalow under the palm trees. With a yearly average of 325 days of sunshine as well as cooling sea breezes, Fabuloso is the ideal destination for a carefree holiday at any time of the year.

Surrounded by warm blue ocean, you can waterski, snorkel and windsurf all year round. Or you can hire a bike and cycle round the whole of Fabuloso in just a day. Or just lie back in your hammock and let the world pass you by. You can't hire a car – because there aren't any! That means no traffic and no rush hour. Just pure peace and relaxation – all day long.

And as the sun sets, you can take a walk along the golden beach and watch the fishermen pulling in their nets. A short stroll takes you into the old town centre where the night air is cool and little restaurants are opening to cook the day's catch.

Fabuloso

Read the text carefully and circle the best ending for each sentence.

1. Fabuloso is
   a) an island.
   b) a hotel.
   c) a theme park.

2. Fabuloso is
   a) very small.
   b) very wet.
   c) very narrow.

3. The air is clean because
   a) it's very breezy.
   b) there's no traffic.
   c) it's by the sea.

4. The nightlife in Fabuloso is
   a) exciting.
   b) quiet.
   c) expensive.

5. If you eat in one of Fabuloso's restaurants,
   you will probably have
   a) pasta.
   b) curry.
   c) seafood.

Express yourself

Think of a place where you have spent a good holiday or choose a place you would like to visit. Write a short holiday brochure to attract people to your holiday destination.

The Mitchell Place

Sent to stay with his aunt in the country while his parents are divorcing, Jake has no idea how he will survive the holidays. Aunt Lou tells him he can roam free but must not go near the old Mitchell place over by the canal. With boarded-up windows, an overgrown garden and a large sign on the fence saying 'Keep Out', the house looks as if no one has been inside for years. Everybody in the village says that terrible things happened there – but no one will say exactly what. This only makes the old house all the more interesting to Jake and the new friends he finds ... It will be a long time before any of them get over what happened in those long hot weeks.

'A thrilling read.
I simply couldn't put it down.'
Anita Webber,
The Reader's Gazette

'Val Watson creates a chilling atmosphere ... there's a heart-stopping revelation in every chapter. Not a book to read alone at night!'
Steve Hogg, Bookworm Times

'Teens will love this gripping tale of friendship, loyalty and fear.'
Rick Latimer, Book Trade

'Another brilliant book from the master of suspense.'
Edmund Critchly,
The Book Reviewer

ISBN 1-85503-383-6

The Mitchell Place

Read the text carefully and circle the best ending for each sentence.

1. The story takes place during
   a) the summer term.
   b) the summer holidays.
   c) the Christmas holidays.

2. At the beginning of the story, Jake is probably worried that he is going to be
   a) ill.
   b) scared.
   c) bored.

3. Jake and his friends probably
   a) stayed away from the Mitchell place.
   b) looked at the Mitchell place through the fence.
   c) explored inside the Mitchell place.

4. Val Watson is
   a) a well-known author.
   b) a new author.
   c) a book reviewer.

5. You would probably find *The Mitchell Place* in a bookshop under
   a) romance.
   b) adventure.
   c) mystery.

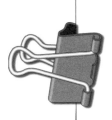

Express yourself

Write a description for the back cover of your favourite book. Your 'blurb' should make everyone want to read it!

Camels

You may have seen camels in films or television programmes about the desert. Sometimes you get shots of them in caravans, moving in a long, slow line across the burning sands, carrying goods and people. Perhaps you can imagine why they were known as 'the ships of the desert'.

Camels are wonderfully suited to life in dry sandy places. Their feet are divided so that they have only two very broad toes, which is ideal for walking on shifting sand. They can also close their nostrils against sand-laden desert winds. Few animals can live for long in hot, dry places where there is almost no water, but camels are specially adapted for such harsh conditions. They do not sweat, so they do not lose any moisture. Their thick coats also help to ensure moisture does not escape from their bodies as well as providing protection from the burning sun in the day and the cold desert nights. They pass very little water as urine, and even the liquid from their nostrils collects in a groove running to their mouths, so it is recycled.

Camels can go for long periods without drinking, but when they do they can consume 57 litres without stopping! Many people think that the camel's hump stores water, but this is not the case. It actually stores fat, which the camel consumes when food is scarce. The hump goes floppy when the fat is used up.

Camels

Read the text carefully and circle the best ending for each sentence.

1) In the passage, a caravan is
   a) a group of people going on holiday.
   b) a line of camels.
   c) a truck for transporting camels.

2) The camel's feet are a good shape for
   a) helping it to slide across the sand.
   b) stopping it from sinking into the sand.
   c) making it sweat less.

3) Because camels do not sweat, they
   a) do not smell.
   b) feel hot all the time.
   c) lose very little water from their bodies.

4) The difference between daytime and night-time temperatures in the desert is
   a) extreme.
   b) slight.
   c) nothing.

5) The camel can store fat in its hump and this is useful because
   a) it stops the hump from going floppy.
   b) water is scarce in the desert.
   c) food is scarce in the desert.

Find out for yourself

There are two different kinds of camel. What are they and how are they different? Which countries would you find each one in? Plan and then write a paragraph comparing the two types.

Lost

I looked down at the hard white peaks beneath me. Snow had gathered thick on the western side, which was now glowing in the setting sun. They were somewhere down there, lost in those snowy valleys, looking up to the skies for help. Perhaps some of their party were injured. Some might already have frostbite after so many hours. And some might even be dead. I did not want to think about that; I had a job to do. But this was not like any other rescue I had been called out on.

I circled lower towards some fir trees, so low that their dark green pointed tops swayed in the wind from the rotor blades. Anyone down there would surely hear me and come running out of the trees, waving their red ski jacket. Anyone alive, that was. If they could run.

With the sun setting lower, the temperature would be falling. I looked at my instruments: thirteen degrees below zero. No one could survive a night on the mountain! I scanned the snow for some sign of life or movement and shouted to Mick behind me to train the searchlight on the trees. I could hear panic in my voice. Our two pairs of eyes were all we had to find them. And Margot was all I had got.

Lost

Read the text carefully and circle the best ending for each sentence.

1. The writer is in
   a) a plane.
   b) a car.
   c) a helicopter.

2. He is a
   a) mountain rescuer.
   b) policeman.
   c) hunter.

3. The lost party were
   a) skiing.
   b) hiking.
   c) hang gliding.

4. This was not like any other rescue for the writer because
   a) it was so cold.
   b) Margot was in the lost party.
   c) it was getting late.

5. The writer is
   a) alone.
   b) with a team of people.
   c) with one other person.

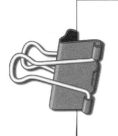

Find out for yourself

In what different situations can people get into danger and need to be rescued? What ways are there to find or rescue people? How can trained animals or technology be helpful?

Burglary

I woke with a start. There was a noise downstairs. At first I thought it must be Jemmy. But I could feel her warm body curled up at the foot of my bed. Nervously, I got up and tiptoed down. I noticed the kitchen light was on. I opened the door very slowly. Nobody was there.

As I went in, I felt immediately that the room was very cold. I glanced round. No windows were open but the fridge door was ajar. I looked inside. Someone had taken a big bite out of the chocolate cake I had bought for a friend's birthday party the next day. Still too sleepy to understand why the room was so cold, I went to check the back door. As I got near, my slippers crunched something underfoot. Glass! And the back door was wide open with the key still in the inside lock. I had been burgled.

I rushed to my study where I keep my cash box inside a locked cupboard. I grabbed the clock off the shelf and checked underneath it for the key. It was still there. What a relief! I didn't bother to open the cupboard; I knew my prize money was safe.

Burglary

Read the text carefully and circle the best ending for each sentence.

1. Jemmy must be the writer's
   a) wife.
   b) pet.
   c) neighbour.

2. The kitchen was cold because
   a) the fridge door was open.
   b) the door to the study was open.
   c) the back door was open.

3. The burglar got in by
   a) breaking the glass in the door and turning the key.
   b) breaking the glass in the window and climbing in.
   c) forcing the lock.

4. The writer did not bother to look in the cupboard for his money because
   a) he knew they had stolen the money.
   b) the money was not kept in the cupboard.
   c) the burglar had not found the key for the cupboard.

5. The cash box contained money that the writer had
   a) earned.
   b) won.
   c) stolen.

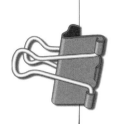

Express yourself

Imagine a noise wakes you up in the night. What sort of noise is it? Could it be a burglar? Or does the noise turn out to be something else? Write a short story about it.

Phone Call

Look carefully at the text and circle the best answer to each question.

Gill Antonio:

Hello, Gill Antonio speaking.

1

   a) Hello, can I speak to Mandy, please?
   b) Hello, is this the pizzeria?
   c) Can I order a taxi for 3 o'clock, please?

Gill Antonio:

No, I'm afraid Mandy is not in. This is her mother. Who is speaking, please?

2

   a) It's Tom.
   b) It's Jennifer.
   c) It's a friend.

Gill Antonio:

Oh hello, Jenny. Can I take a message for her?

3

   a) No, it's okay. I'll call later.
   b) Can you tell her she's invited to my party on Friday?
   c) Can she come to the cinema tonight?

Gill Antonio:

Certainly, but I know she's got drama club on that day.

④

a) I've got swimming club.
b) It's my birthday, you see.
c) Drama club is great!

Gill Antonio:

Oh, is it? Happy birthday! What time is this party?

⑤

a) It starts at 7.30.
b) No special time.
c) Eight o'clock.

Gill Antonio:

Well, drama club finishes at 7.30, so she might make it by then. Thank you – I'll let her know, Jenny. Goodbye!

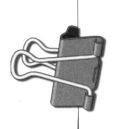

Express yourself

Write a short dialogue between two people. Then write it out again, but leave out all of one person's words so that you see one side of the conversation only. Give it to a friend to read and ask them to try and write in the missing words. How close is their version to the original script?

The Mission

Chief: Now listen carefully, Smith. Your future – and the future of this country – may depend on it.

Smith: I'm listening, Chief.

Chief: When your train arrives at the station, their agent will be there to meet you. She'll be wearing a white coat and will carry a red bag. Go to the station restaurant and sit at the table nearest the window. After a few minutes she will join you.

Smith: Then what do I say to her?

Chief: Tell her you have brought what they want. Here's the briefcase. You can show her what's in it, but don't let her have it until she has given you what we want. You'd better look inside now.

Smith: There's at least … five hundred thousand here!

Chief: Well, a million, to be precise – in used notes. Now, before you hand it all over, you must examine the plans she has brought and make sure they are the real thing. We're depending on you, Smith. Only you know exactly what the plans should look like.

Smith: I see.

Chief: Once you have the plans, you must make your way straight back. But be on your guard. We don't know who will be watching – and if those plans were to fall into the wrong hands …

Smith: I understand.

Chief: I hope you do, Smith. If there is any mistake, then …

Smith: Don't worry, Chief – the mission is in safe hands. I'll come back with those plans, or my name isn't Smith!

Chief: It isn't – that's your codename!

Smith: Ah!

The Mission

Read the text carefully and circle the best ending for each sentence.

1. Chief is Smith's
   a) friend.
   b) boss.
   c) father.

2. The briefcase contains
   a) money.
   b) diamonds.
   c) lottery tickets.

3. Chief wants Smith to make sure that the plans are
   a) neatly drawn.
   b) not stolen.
   c) not fake.

4. Chief is worried that once Smith has got the plans,
   a) he might run off with them.
   b) someone might try to get them from him.
   c) he might leave them on the train.

5. The Chief's mission makes Smith feel
   a) afraid.
   b) angry.
   c) determined.

Express yourself

What do you think the plans are for? Write the dialogue that takes place in the railway station between Smith and the agent. Does the meeting go according to plan or does something unexpected happen?

Barbecued Chicken

Ingredients

8 chicken pieces

1 garlic clove, crushed

$\frac{1}{4}$ cup freshly squeezed
   lemon juice

2 tablespoons olive oil

2 teaspoons ground pepper

2 tablespoons freshly chopped
   parsley

$\frac{1}{2}$ teaspoon chilli powder

pinch of salt

In a food processor, blend the chilli powder, garlic, olive oil, lemon juice and parsley into a smooth paste. Rub this mixture into the chicken, making sure you coat it completely. Leave the coated chicken pieces to marinate for at least 3 hours in the fridge.

Start the charcoal fire and let the coals burn down to grey ash. Preheat the oven to 180 °C/ gas mark 4.

Season the chicken pieces then place them on the barbecue about 12 cm above the coals. Barbecue the chicken for about 20 minutes, turning frequently until all the sides appear slightly charred. Transfer the barbecued chicken to a large roasting tin, cover loosely with kitchen foil and finish cooking in the oven until tender (about 30 minutes). Remove and serve with French bread and salads.

Health tip: Cut down your fat intake! Remove the skin from the chicken pieces before coating with the barbecue paste.

Barbecued Chicken

Fill in the gaps, choosing the best word or phrase from the text.

① Apart from the chicken, the only ingredients that do not go into the food

processor are _____ and _____ .

② The chicken is cooked on the barbecue for _____ and in

the oven for _____ .

③ You know the chicken has been on the barbecue long enough because it

looks _____ .

④ It is healthier to remove the chicken skin because it contains a lot of

_____ .

⑤ To make this recipe you would need a barbecue, an oven and a fridge.

Other equipment you would need is _____, a

_____ and some _____ .

Find out for yourself

It is not healthy to eat too much fat. What else should you do to eat healthily? Find out what foods you need for a balanced diet.

Jetcar Set to Take Off

Traffic jams could soon be a thing of the past, thanks to a new high-flying invention from an American technology company. The Jetcar looks set to take off in a big way – and TJC, the Texas-based company, say they are receiving floods of enquiries from an eager public.

Resembling a conventional four-seater plane rather than a family saloon, the Jetcar is designed for use both on the road and in the air. On the road it behaves very much like a normal car and has a top speed of 65 mph. When it takes to the sky, it can soar to over 3,000 metres, reaching a maximum speed of 400 mph. The higher you go, the thinner the air becomes and the faster the Jetcar can travel.

With a wingspan of just 3 metres, the Jetcar is much smaller than a conventional aircraft, but as it has a length of over 7 metres, owners will probably have to rebuild their garages.

The Jetcar is all set to go – but it's not off the ground yet. Before would-be owners can take their first air-ride, the company needs to get permission from civil aviation authorities who are very worried about the risk of air accidents. How many air traffic controllers will we need if we are all taking to the sky every time we get stuck in a jam?

Jetcar Set to Take Off

Fill in the gaps, choosing the best word or phrase from the text.

1 Jetcars could be a way of avoiding _____ .

2 The Jetcar does not really look like a typical _____ .

3 The fastest a Jetcar can travel is _____ on the road and

_____ in the air.

4 The vehicle measures approximately _____ by

_____.

5 The main problem with Jetcars is the danger of _____ .

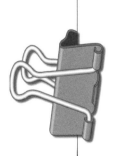

Express yourself

Make a list of problems traffic causes. Then invent something to solve one of these problems. It could be a new vehicle or something to help with parking or traffic jams. It might be something to make traffic safer, cleaner, or less noisy.

Make a drawing of your design and think of a good name for it. Label or write a short description of your invention to show clearly what it does.

I Have a Dream!

Dr Martin Luther King was a black preacher who campaigned in the 1960s for the rights of black Americans. At that time, some of the southern American states had laws that meant black citizens were treated very unfairly. In Dr King's state of Alabama, the city buses had separate seats for black and white passengers. Black passengers were only allowed to sit at the back of the bus. If the bus was crowded, they had to give up their seats for white passengers. Martin Luther King organised a boycott of the city buses: black passengers refused to use them and walked to work instead. In the end, the bus company was losing so much money in fares, it let black passengers sit anywhere. The boycott was a non-violent protest against an unfair law.

In August 1963, 200,000 Americans, white and black, marched with Martin Luther King to Washington to hear him give a speech which has become world famous:

> *I have a dream ... that my four little children will one day live in a nation where they will be judged not by the colour of their skin but by the content of their character ... I have a dream, that one day on the red hills of Georgia, the sons of former slaves and the sons of former slave owners will be able to sit down together at the table of brotherhood ... I have a dream!*

Shortly after making this speech, Martin Luther King was killed by a white gunman.

I Have a Dream!

Fill in the gaps, choosing the best word or phrase from the text.

1. In the 1960s, black people were treated badly in

_____ .

2. On the buses in Alabama, black people had to

_____ and _____

_____ .

3. When black people stopped using the buses, it was a form of

_____ .

4. Martin Luther King thought people should be judged by their

_____ and not by _____

_____ .

5. Martin Luther King gave his famous speech in

_____ in the year _____ .

Express yourself

Do you know about an unfair situation? It may be something in your neighbourhood. It may be a problem somewhere else in the world. What is unfair about it? Write a short speech about how you hope the situation will become fairer.

Home!

The exciting race game for 2–4 players

Ages 4 and upwards

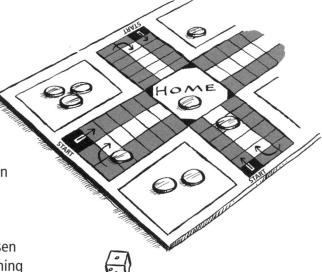

Contents
Playing board with die
16 playing pieces (in 4 colours)

Object of the game
To be the first to get all your counters
once round the track and then HOME in
the centre of the board.

How to play
1. Take the four counters of your chosen
    colour and place them in the matching
    colour corner of the board.
2. Each player throws the die. The player
    who throws the highest number goes first.
    Play continues in a clockwise direction.
3. On your turn, throw the die. You must throw a 6 before you can move a
    counter to your coloured START with the arrow. When you have thrown
    a 6, you may throw again and move this counter forward in a clockwise
    direction the number shown on the die.
4. Once you have a counter already on the track and you throw a 6, you
    may choose **either** to bring another counter out onto the START **or** to
    move a counter already on the track. Remember, if you throw a 6 you
    always get another go.
5. If you land on a space already occupied by an opponent's counter, you
    send that counter back to your opponent's START and take its place.
6. When you have moved a counter all the way around the track once,
    follow the arrow to the HOME square at the centre of the board.
    To move a counter onto the HOME square, you must throw
    the exact number of spaces. If you have not thrown the exact number
    needed, the counter stays on that space and you must wait until your
    next turn to try again.

The winner
The first player to get all four counters HOME wins the game.

Home!

Fill in the gaps, choosing the best word or phrase from the text.

1 The game is designed for a maximum of _____ players.

2 Each player has _____ counters which move once round the track,

travelling _____ .

3 If you throw a 6 you can choose what to do – but only if you have

_____ .

4 If another player lands on the space you are on, you must go

_____ .

5 To move a counter onto the HOME square, you must have

_____ .

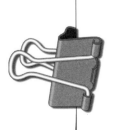

Express yourself

Design a simple board game. What is the object of your game? What will your board look like? Will you need dice? Decide on some rules and write them out clearly for everyone to understand. Give your game a good name.

Fingerprints

If you look closely at your fingertips, you will see a pattern in the skin. If you look very closely, you can also see that each of your fingers has a slightly different pattern. Everyone's fingerprints are unique. That means that nobody else has fingerprints exactly like yours. But what are these patterns for? Why do we have them?

We receive a lot of information through our sense of touch: is something hot or cold, rough or smooth? The skin on the tips of our fingers contains tiny nerve endings which make them sensitive to the slightest difference. The little ridges in the patterns increase the surface area. This means there is more skin – and there are therefore more nerve endings – than if your fingertips were smooth.

There are four basic types of fingerprint: arches, whorls, loops and composites. When we touch anything, we leave behind tiny traces of sweat in the pattern of our fingerprints. This can be very useful in solving crimes. At the scene of a burglary, for example, the police dust all the surfaces with a special aluminium powder. If anyone has touched them, this makes the fingerprints show up clearly. If the fingerprints appear to match those of a suspect, this may be used as evidence in court. However, fingerprint experts have to examine the patterns very carefully and this involves a lot of detailed, scientific work to ensure that matches are correct.

Fingerprints

Fill in the gaps, choosing the best word or phrase from the text.

1 Fingertips can tell us whether something feels _____

   or _____ .

2 The ridges on our fingertips increase the number of

   _____ which makes the skin more sensitive.

3 A fingerprint is actually a pattern made by _____ .

4 _____ is used by police to reveal the

   fingerprints at the scene of a crime.

5 Fingerprints may be used as _____ to help convict a

   suspect.

Find out for yourself

Compare your own fingerprints with the diagrams. Which fingerprint type do you think you have? Do a survey of your class. Which pattern is the most common? Which is the least common? Make a chart to show your results.

Coral

You probably know that coral is something that grows underwater in weird and wonderful shapes and colours. It is easy to imagine that coral is a plant of some kind. But in fact, coral is made up of thousands of small creatures called polyps.

The polyp is a soft, sac-like animal, a bit like a sea anemone. There are many different kinds, some only a few millimetres long, others a few centimetres. There are millions of polyp larvae (young polyps) drifting in the warm tropical seas. These can attach themselves to rocks and grow together to form a colony. The adult polyps form hard, limestone skeletons around their soft bodies and this forms the structure of the coral.

Over the years the colony grows, with new polyps growing on the skeletons of the old ones. The growth is slow, however, with most corals growing about 2 cm a year. Some of these colonies have been growing for hundreds or even thousands of years, with new living coral being built up on layers of dead coral. When this happens, it is called a reef. The most famous example of this is probably the Great Barrier Reef on the east coast of Australia. Spanning 2,000 kilometres (1,250 miles), this is the only living thing that can be seen from the moon.

Coral needs clear water and sunlight, so reefs grow in shallow waters. This is why many are found attached to the rocks around an island or continent.

Although coral reefs have been around for so long, their future looks extremely uncertain. Much of the world's coral is being destroyed by fishing and pollution. Also, coral is very sensitive to temperature change – and a rise in sea temperatures looks likely as a result of global warming.

Coral

Fill in the gaps, choosing the best word or phrase from the text.

1. Coral is not a plant but a _____ of small animals called polyps.

2. The polyps have an external skeleton made of _____ .

3. Coral reefs are usually _____ of years old.

4. The most well-known coral reef can be found _____ _____ .

5. Coral is under threat from _____ , _____ and _____ .

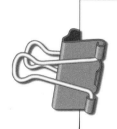

Find out for yourself

What is a coral atoll and how does it form? Draw some diagrams to show what happens.

Zap-132
User Guide

Thank you for choosing a Zap-132 mobile phone. You can now enter the world of Zap communication and take advantage of the very latest advances in mobile technology.

SAFETY

Before you start, please read these simple guidelines. Failure to observe them may be dangerous or illegal.

 Always use the phone in a normal operating position (to your ear).

 Use only approved batteries and accessories. Other products may be incompatible with the Zap-132 and may affect the phone's performance.

 Dispose of used batteries safely.

 Avoid use of the phone while driving; park your vehicle first. Using a hand-held phone while driving is illegal and can affect your concentration. Road safety comes first.

 Using a phone when airborne is illegal and can interfere with the plane's computer. Switch the phone off in an aircraft.

 Switch the phone off near flammable substances, e.g. petrol stations, fuel depots and chemical plants.

 Switch the phone off in a hospital; it may interfere with medical equipment.

 Keep your phone in a safe place, out of reach of small children. The SIM card in your mobile phone can be removed. This may represent a choking hazard.

Zap-132 User Guide

Fill in the gaps, choosing the best word or phrase from the text.

1. The phone's performance may be affected by _____

_____ .

2. You will be breaking the law if you use a hand-held phone while

_____ or _____ .

3. The phone should be always switched off _____ ,

_____ and

_____ .

4. If your phone is on in a hospital it may _____

_____ .

5. It would be possible for a small child to choke on _____ .

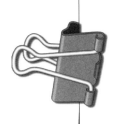

Express yourself

Write safety instructions for some equipment you have used. It could be a watch, a CD player or a swimming pool. What should the user do for it to be safe? What should they not do? What could happen? Set out your instructions so they are easy to understand.

Fill in the gaps, choosing the best word or phrase from the list of possible answers.

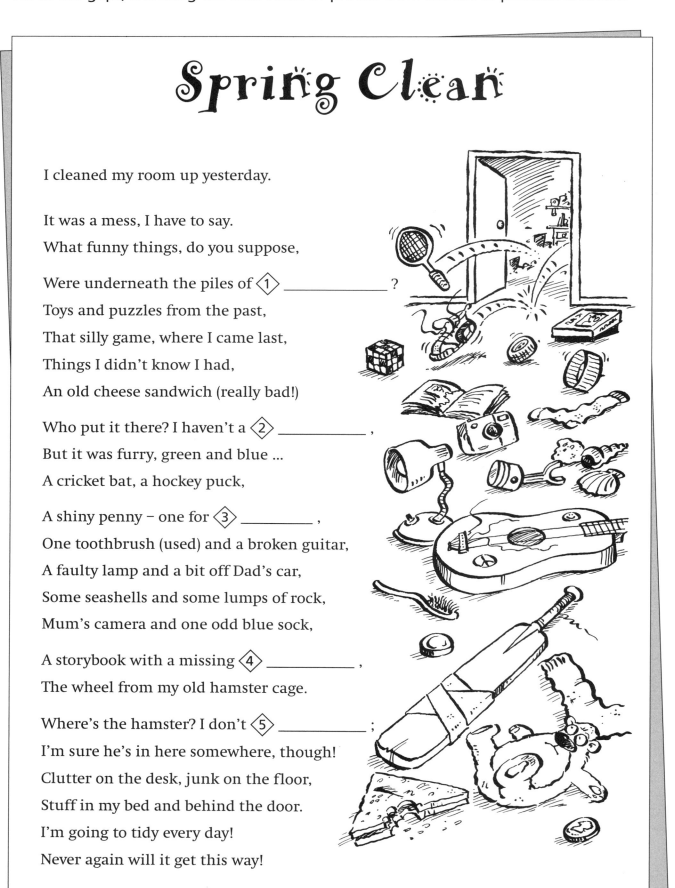

Spring Clean

I cleaned my room up yesterday.

It was a mess, I have to say.
What funny things, do you suppose,

Were underneath the piles of ⟨1⟩ _____ ?
Toys and puzzles from the past,
That silly game, where I came last,
Things I didn't know I had,
An old cheese sandwich (really bad!)

Who put it there? I haven't a ⟨2⟩ _____ ,
But it was furry, green and blue ...
A cricket bat, a hockey puck,

A shiny penny – one for ⟨3⟩ _____ ,
One toothbrush (used) and a broken guitar,
A faulty lamp and a bit off Dad's car,
Some seashells and some lumps of rock,
Mum's camera and one odd blue sock,

A storybook with a missing ⟨4⟩ _____ ,
The wheel from my old hamster cage.

Where's the hamster? I don't ⟨5⟩ _____ ;
I'm sure he's in here somewhere, though!
Clutter on the desk, junk on the floor,
Stuff in my bed and behind the door.
I'm going to tidy every day!
Never again will it get this way!

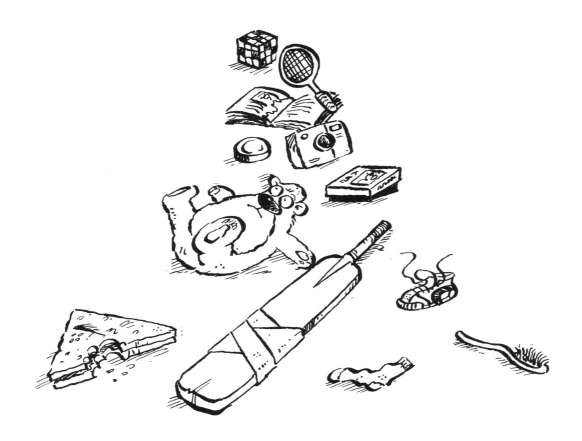

Spring Clean

① a) junk   b) stuff   c) rubbish   d) clothes

② a) shoe   b) clue   c) thought   d) notion

③ a) luck   b) Grandma   c) spending   d) me

④ a) chapter   b) cover   c) stage   d) page

⑤ a) care   b) cough   c) know   d) go

Ask yourself

Who does the housework in your house? Who does the cooking and washing? Who takes care of the garden? Are the jobs shared fairly in your family?

Fill in the gaps, choosing the best word or phrase from the list of possible answers.

Grape Picking in France

France is the largest country in western Europe. It is also one of the world's leading wine producers. The different grape varieties as well as the varied ⟨1⟩ _____ and climates of France produce many different kinds of wine.

Most grapes are picked in late September, at the end of the growing season. Harvesting is still done almost totally by ⟨2⟩ _____ . Many young people spend their holidays grape picking. It is very hard work! Grape pickers carry a heavy basket on their backs and must bend down to get the ⟨3⟩ _____ growing on the low vines.

In the past, juice from the harvested grapes was pressed by ⟨4⟩ _____ . Workers would get into wooden barrels and tread the grapes until the juice ran out. Today, the process is much more ⟨5⟩ _____ ! Large industrial presses are used to extract the juice, which is then stored in stainless steel vats.

Grape Picking in France

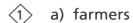

①	a) farmers	b) shops	c) soils	d) earth
②	a) hand	b) machine	c) winter	d) now
③	a) food	b) ground	c) flowers	d) fruit
④	a) foot	b) hand	c) men	d) women
⑤	a) expensive	b) rapid	c) interesting	d) hygienic

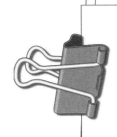

Find out for yourself

Find out more about the process of winemaking. Draw a flow diagram to show the different stages.

Fill in the gaps, choosing the best word or phrase from the list of possible answers.

Vegetarians

'Suitable for vegetarians'. You have probably seen these words and the vegetarian symbol on food packaging in the supermarket. There are many people who are vegetarian. Some choose not to eat meat products because they believe that farming and killing animals for food is morally wrong. Some do not eat meat because of their religious ◇1◇ _____ , while others choose a meat-free ◇2◇ _____ because they believe it is healthier. You probably know people who are vegetarians or may be one yourself.

As long as they eat a balanced diet with enough protein, vegetarians can obtain all the nutrients they need. Eggs, dairy products, pulses and nuts are all good sources of protein.

There are also some excellent ◇3◇ _____ to meat such as soya and tofu – and 'veggie burgers' are great on the barbecue. Eating out is not a ◇4◇ _____ as most restaurant menus these days have a 'veggie' option.

One group of very ◇5◇ _____ vegetarians, called vegans, do not eat animal products of any kind, even milk and cheese.

Vegetarians

1.   a) beliefs   b) believe   c) fears   d) festivals

2.   a) sausage   b) shop   c) diet   d) religion

3.   a) alternatives   b) alternates   c) attractions   d) additions

4.   a) treat   b) decision   c) possibility   d) problem

5.   a) nice   b) strict   c) hard   d) boring

Ask yourself

Is it right to kill animals for their meat? Is it right to farm animals for their milk or eggs?

Fill in the gaps, choosing the best word or phrase from the list of possible answers.

Room 221

① _____ Ocean View Hotel.

Our friendly staff are here to serve you and ensure that your stay in the Ocean

View Hotel is as pleasant and comfortable as ② _____ .

Please take a minute to read this brochure and acquaint yourself

with the services available.

Restaurants

Ocean View has two top-class restaurants and two lively bars.

Breakfast is served between 8 and 10 o'clock on the Hummingbird Terrace,

③ _____ the sea. You may choose a full English or a

continental breakfast, both with a selection of tropical fruits and fruit juices.

Lunch (12–2 pm) and dinner (7–9 pm) are both served in the Mango Tree

Restaurant on the ground floor.

Light snacks can be ordered at any time in the Pirates' Bar.

Please note that beachwear is not permitted in the hotel bars and

restaurants. However, the Surfers' Bar on the beach will always be happy

to ④ _____ you.

Room Service

Call 01 to order food, newspaper delivery, personal laundry or

other room services.

Island Tours

These are led by experienced guides in fully air-conditioned buses.

Departure is from the hotel foyer at 10 am ⑤ _____ .

Further details are available at the Reception desk.

Ocean View Hotel   Palm Tree Avenue   Barbados

Ocean View Hotel is part of The Maddison Hotel Group.

Room 221

①	a) This is	b) Here is	c) We present	d) Welcome to
②	a) ever	b) much	c) possible	d) far
③	a) overlooking	b) on top of	c) away from	d) nearby
④	a) dress	b) feed	c) serve	d) inform
⑤	a) regularly	b) sometimes	c) nightly	d) daily

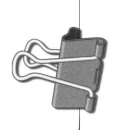

Find out for yourself

Where is the island this hotel is on? Look in an atlas to find out. What is the name of the group of islands it belongs to?

Fill in the gaps, choosing the best word or phrase from the list of possible answers.

Space Exploration

People have always been fascinated by the heavens. Four
thousand years ago, the ancient Egyptians built their pyramids
so that they lined up with certain constellations or groups of
①_____. Since ancient times, people have
dreamed about exploring space, but it was only in the mid-
20th century that space flight became a ②_____.
This was a result of two important inventions. The first was a
powerful engine that could blast the spacecraft away from
the Earth and also work in the vacuum of space where there
is no atmosphere. This invention was the rocket engine. The
③_____ was the modern computer, which was
necessary for controlling and guiding the entire mission from
lift-off to re-entry.

The first space missions were launched by the Soviet Union and
the United States in hot ④_____ with each other.
This came to be called the 'space race'. These early missions
were aimed mainly at exploring our own moon.

Today many countries participate in the exploration of space; there is co-operation rather than competition between different ⟨5⟩ _____ . Missions go far beyond the moon, as unmanned spacecraft are sent to other planets in the solar system and then flung out into the galaxy. But as well as reaching to the stars, spacecraft also carry up satellites that look back at the Earth, gathering important information that will help us understand and manage our own planet.

Space Exploration

⟨1⟩ a) clouds   b) stars   c) kings   d) mountains

⟨2⟩ a) problem   b) desire   c) reality   d) interest

⟨3⟩ a) last   b) first   c) second   d) best

⟨4⟩ a) battle   b) rockets   c) committee   d) competition

⟨5⟩ a) nations   b) planets   c) rockets   d) astronauts

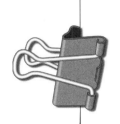

Ask yourself

Some millionaires are now paying to spend a few days in space. Would you like to go? Do you think that one day we will all be able to have 'space holidays'? What could you see or do in space? What problems might there be?

Fill in the gaps, choosing the best word or phrase from the list of possible answers.

Skateboarding
for Beginners

Hey! If you want to skateboard but don't know how to start, this is for you! Here are the basics …

Let's start with the ⟨1⟩ _____ . It's made of a wooden base called a 'deck'. It's covered in grip tape. On the bottom it's got metal holders to hold the wheels on. Except the wheels are called 'trucks'. But that's about it!

Now, let's look at some ⟨2⟩ _____ . The most basic one is an 'ollie'. This is when you do a jump on your skateboard. If you can't ollie – well then you can't skate, dude! So, place your strongest foot at the back of the deck, put your other foot in the middle of the grip tape, and then bend your knees and jump up. You should land back on the board. Got it … ? No? Well, try again.

Unless you are ⟨3⟩ _____ to be a pro,

you won't manage it the first time. But hey!

Keep practising!

Once you can ollie, you'll want to move on to more advanced stuff!

If you get hold of a sheet of plywood and some bricks, you can make a really

④ _____ ramp (it's called a 'half-pipe'). Smooth down the end of the

plywood with sandpaper so you can ride up it easily. Then it makes a great ramp for

skating!

If you can find a metal pole or a rail, you can lay it down on some steps and

'grind' down it. Wa-hey! Have fun, ⑤ _____ !

Skateboarding for Beginners

① a) clothes   b) board   c) lesson   d) wheels

② a) ideas   b) skateboards   c) moves   d) trucks

③ a) paid   b) taught   c) old enough   d) born

④ a) fascinating   b) cool   c) expensive   d) dangerous

⑤ a) chum   b) sir   c) dude   d) dear

Express yourself

Have you learned how to do something recently? It could be a sport, a game or a hobby that requires a particular skill. Write a short article explaining the basics to a beginner.

Fill in the gaps, choosing the best word or phrase from the list of possible answers.

Bob Marley

Say 'reggae' and most people instantly think of two things: Bob Marley and Jamaica. Bob Marley was the young Jamaican who made reggae music ⟨1⟩ _____ all round the world. He was born to a black mother and a white father on the West Indian island in 1945. When Bob was 10, he and his mother moved from the countryside to Kingston, the capital. They lived in a ⟨2⟩ _____ area called Trenchtown. Living conditions were hard for the young Bob Marley.

When he was only 15, Bob joined a group called the Wailers and started to write and sing songs about Trenchtown life. The band quickly rose to fame in the Caribbean. Eventually, a recording contract with an international record company meant that the face of the young Jamaican with dreadlocks was ⟨3⟩ _____ around the world.

Marley's reggae sound, which grew out of the local rhythms of Trenchtown, became known and hummed by young people from Russia to Japan. In 1976, a gunman tried to kill Bob Marley because he ⟨4⟩_____ to take sides with any of the town's violent gangs. We can only imagine what hits Bob Marley would have gone on to write if he had not contracted cancer of the foot. It spread through his body and, sadly, the brilliant ⟨5⟩_____ lost his battle with the disease in 1981. The grave where Bob Marley is buried in Jamaica is now a national shrine.

Bob Marley

⟨1⟩   a) admitted   b) discussed   c) popular   d) danced

⟨2⟩   a) rough   b) rich   c) central   d) nice

⟨3⟩   a) searched   b) heard   c) copied   d) recognised

⟨4⟩   a) agreed   b) refused   c) decided   d) departed

⟨5⟩   a) player   b) composer   c) singer   d) singer–composer

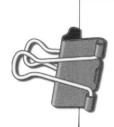

Find out for yourself

Listen to a Bob Marley song. What do you think it is about? Is it happy or sad?

Answers

Getting the main idea

Up and Away

1) a. 2) c. 3) b. 4) a. 5) c.

Hungry World Sponsored Walk

1) b. 2) b. 3) c. 4) a. 5) b.

Film Review

1) a. 2) b. 3) c. 4) b. 5) b.

Ali's Reply

1) b. 2) c. 3) b. 4) a. 5) c.

John Lennon

1) c. 2) b. 3) c. 4) a. 5) b.

The Stash

1) b. 2) b. 3) c. 4) c. 5) b.

Braille

1) b. 2) b. 3) c. 4) b. 5) a.

Anne Frank

1) b. 2) c. 3) c. 4) a. 5) b.

Making inferences

Fabuloso

1) a. 2) a. 3) b. 4) b. 5) c.

The Mitchell Place

1) b. 2) c. 3) c. 4) a. 5) c.

Camels

1) b. 2) b. 3) c. 4) a. 5) c.

Lost

1) c. 2) a. 3) a. 4) b. 5) c.

Burglary

1) b. 2) c. 3) a. 4) c. 5) b.

Phone Call

1) a. 2) b. 3) b. 4) b. 5) c.

The Mission

1) b. 2) a. 3) c. 4) b. 5) c.

Noting details

Barbecued Chicken

1) a pinch of salt, 2 teaspoons ground pepper 2) 20 minutes, 30 minutes 3) slightly charred 4) fat 5) a food processor, a large roasting tin, kitchen foil

Jetcar Set to Take Off

1) traffic jams
2) family saloon
3) 65 mph, 400 mph
4) 3 metres, 7 metres
5) air accidents

I Have a Dream!

1) the southern American states 2) sit at the back, give up their seats for white passengers 3) non-violent protest 4) character, the colour of their skin 5) Washington, 1963

Home!

1) four 2) four, clockwise 3) a counter already on the track 4) back to the start 5) the exact number

Fingerprints

1) hot or cold, rough or smooth 2) nerve endings 3) sweat 4) aluminium powder 5) evidence

Coral

1) colony 2) limestone 3) hundreds or even thousands 4) on the east coast of Australia 5) fishing, pollution, global warming /a rise in sea temperatures

Zap-132 User Guide

1) incompatible batteries or accessories
2) driving, airborne
3) in an aircraft, near flammable substances, in a hospital
4) interfere with medical equipment
5) the SIM card

Using context clues

Spring Clean

1) d. 2) b. 3) a. 4) d. 5) c.

Grape Picking in France

1) c. 2) a. 3) d. 4) a. 5) d.

Vegetarians

1) a. 2) c. 3) a. 4) d. 5) b.

Room 221

1) d. 2) c. 3) a. 4) c. 5) d.

Space Exploration

1) b. 2) c. 3) c. 4) d. 5) a.

Skateboarding for Beginners

1) b. 2) c. 3) d. 4) b. 5) c.

Bob Marley

1) c. 2) a. 3) d. 4) b. 5) d.